KU-499-612

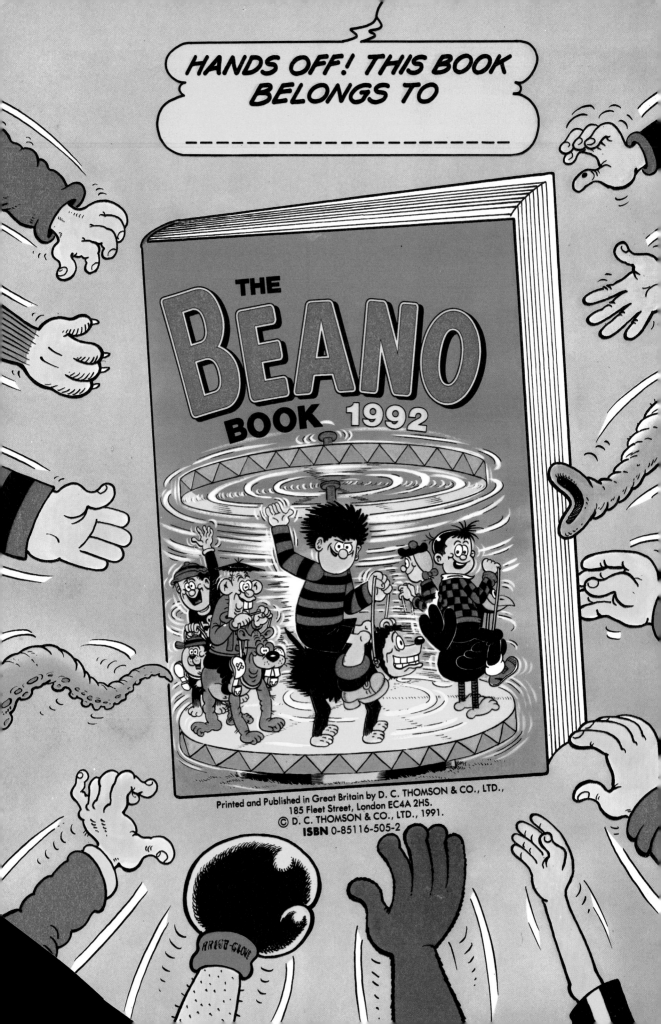

I'LL TAKE SOME TEA TO TEACHER.

GASP!

HELP! HELP! GET AWAY FROM ME YOU HORRIBLE MONSTER!

Teacher was here

HOW DARE YOU SAY THAT!

THUMP!

EH? WHAT? WHERE AM I?

OH, DEAR — YOU MUST HAVE HAD A NIGHTMARE!

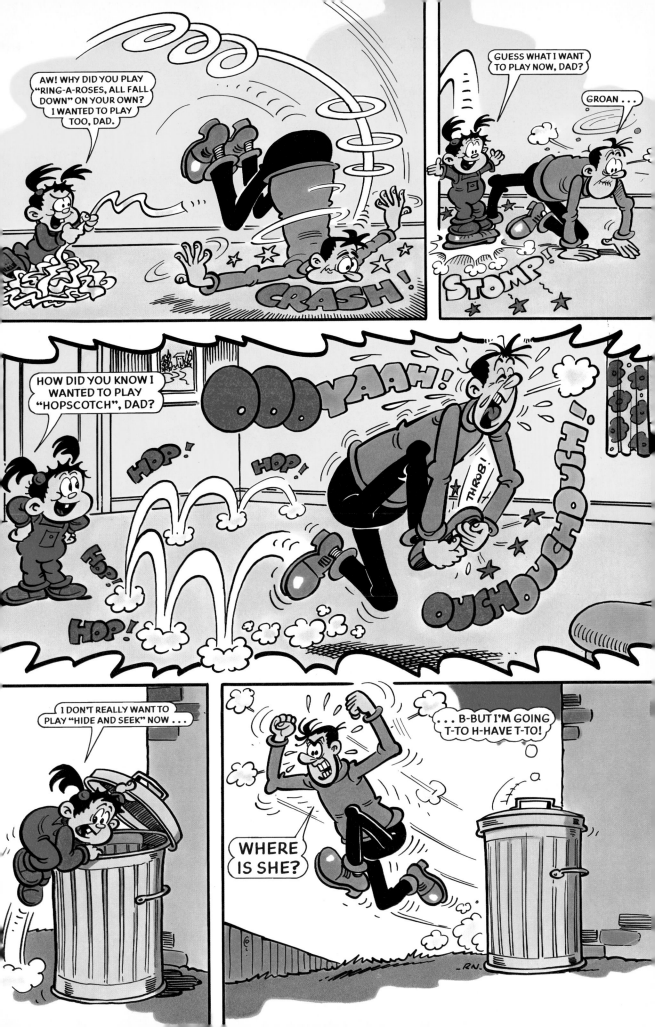

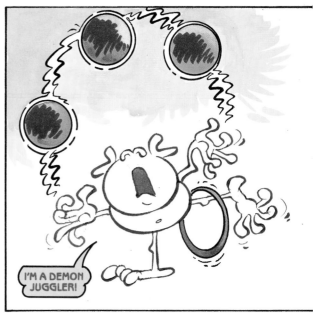

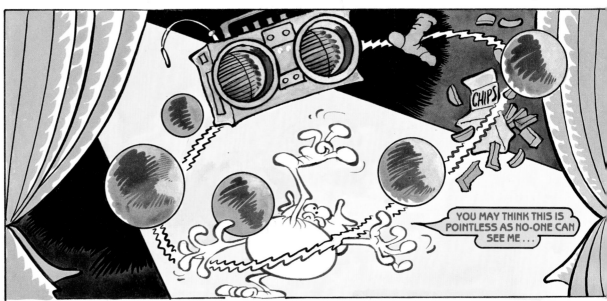

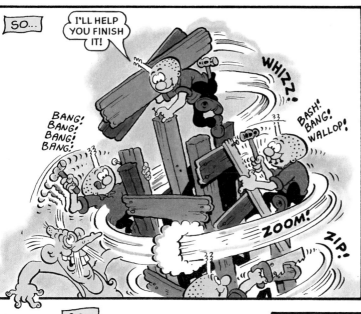

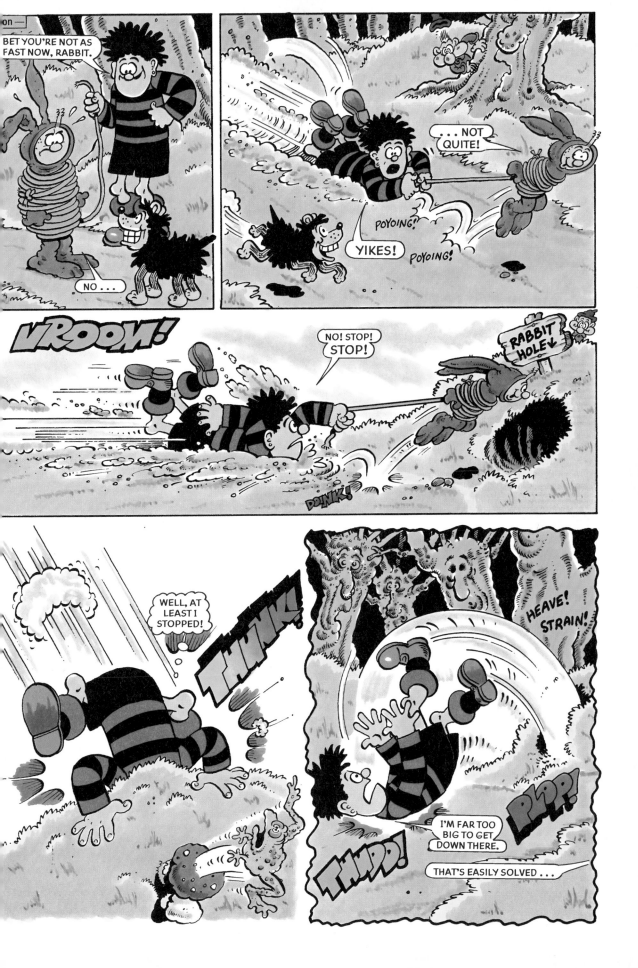

At the local baths —

BLOW!

WOW! INDOOR WIND SURFING.

I WONDER WHAT OTHER OUTDOOR SPORTS COULD BE DONE INDOORS?

I KNOW!

ICE CREAM

MORE

EVEN MORE

UP YOU GO, FATTY.

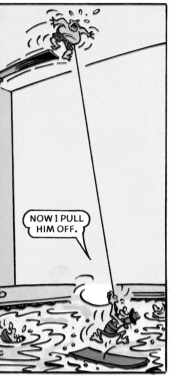

BABY-FACE

FINLAYSON

The Prince made up for lost time —

Then the wicked witch returned —

The witch cursed the Prince again —

And they all lived happily ever after!

DENNIS and PETS

WHO'LL LOOK AFTER MY PETS WHILE I'M AWAY ON HOLIDAY?

WE WILL! WE WILL!

WELL, MY PETS SEEM TO LIKE YOU.

Then —

IT'S THE 3 BEARS AGAIN!

NNNGH! THIS IS HEAVY!

GRUNT!

STRAIN!

HELLO, ROGER. CAN I HELP?

THANK YOU, MISTER WILSON!

STRUGLE!

Roger's next door neighbour.

PHEW! STILL DODGING ARE YOU? WHAT'S YOUR FAVOURITE DODGE?

IT COULD BE THE EMPTY FISH TANK DODGE.

I SAID IT WAS FULL OF 'JAPANESE INVISIBLE FISH' AND CHARGED A SWEET EACH FOR WATCHING THEM!

WHAT NICE FISH!

WOW!

HA-HA!

GENERAL JUMBO

JUMBO JOHNSON had his own private army, navy and airforce — lous models built by his friend essor Carter. Jumbo was testing ew squadron of Motor Torpedo ts on the river running through Dinchester Common.

SWITCHING TO FULL POWER, PROFESSOR! LOOK AT THEM GO!

I'VE INCORPORATED A NEW TURBO-JET IN THESE MODELS, JUMBO.

her up the river—

YIPES! WE'RE UNDER ATTACK!

SORRY, LADS. I DIDN'T MEAN TO DISTURB YOUR FISHING.

Jumbo suspended the trials.

YOU DIDN'T DISTURB THE FISH, JUMBO. THERE AREN'T ANY. NOT LIVE ONES, ANYWAY. LOOK!

YOU MEAN SOMETHING IS KILLING THE FISH? I'LL TAKE A WATER SAMPLE.

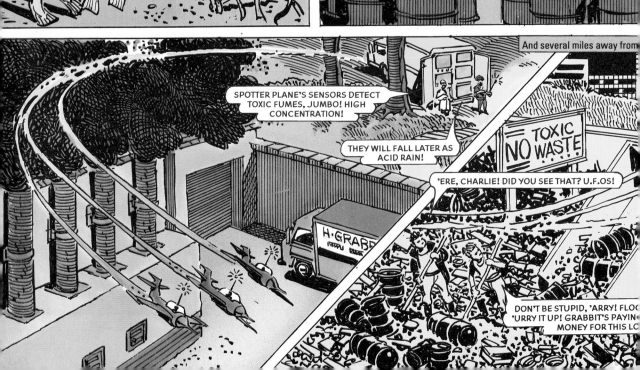

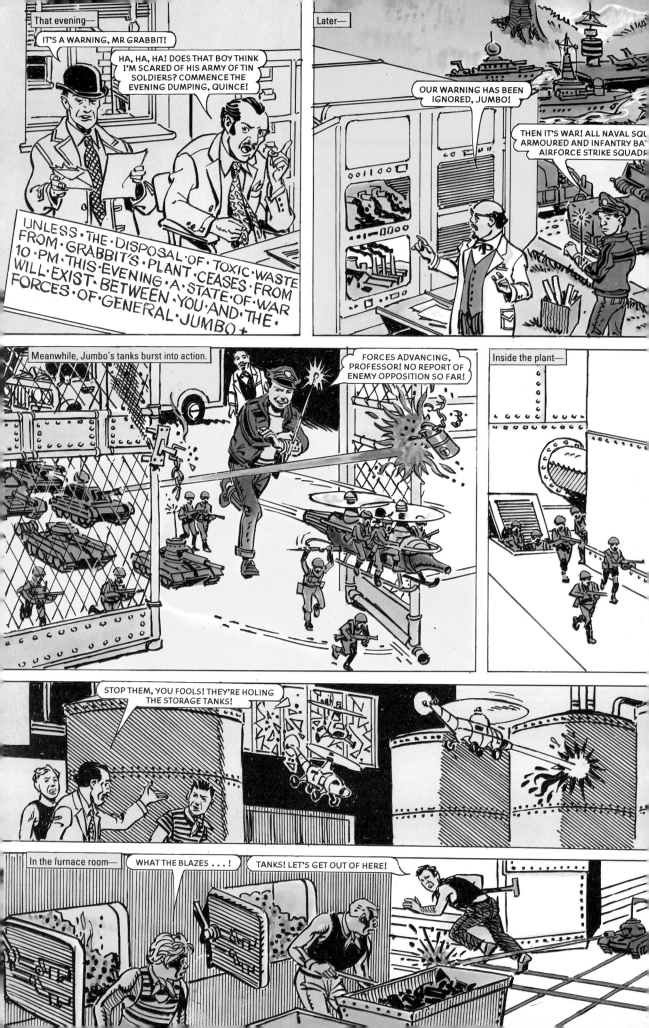

Jumbo's forces closed in for the assault.

...GOT RID OF THAT LITTLE LOT! ...S ARE READY FOR REFILLING NOW!

YIPES! WHAT'S THIS! WE'RE BEING ATTACKED!

CALL MR GRABBIT!

The pellets fired by the frogmen stung the bemused workmen.

Jumbo punched buttons on his arm control gadget.

AUXILIARY FIRE-FIGHTING UNIT IN POSITION, PROFESSOR! AM ACTIVATING!

The furnace was soon damped down.

YAAAAH!

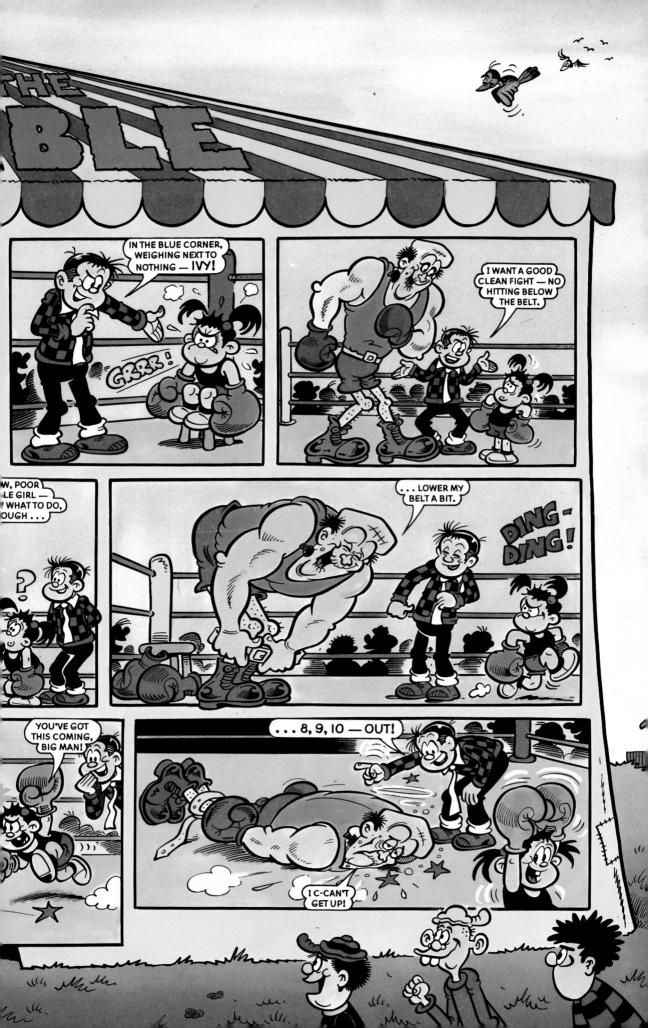

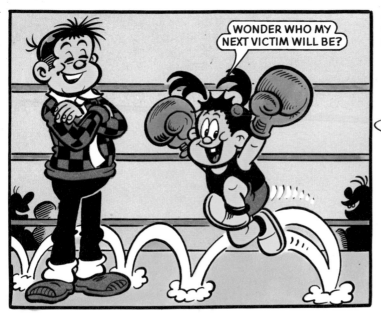

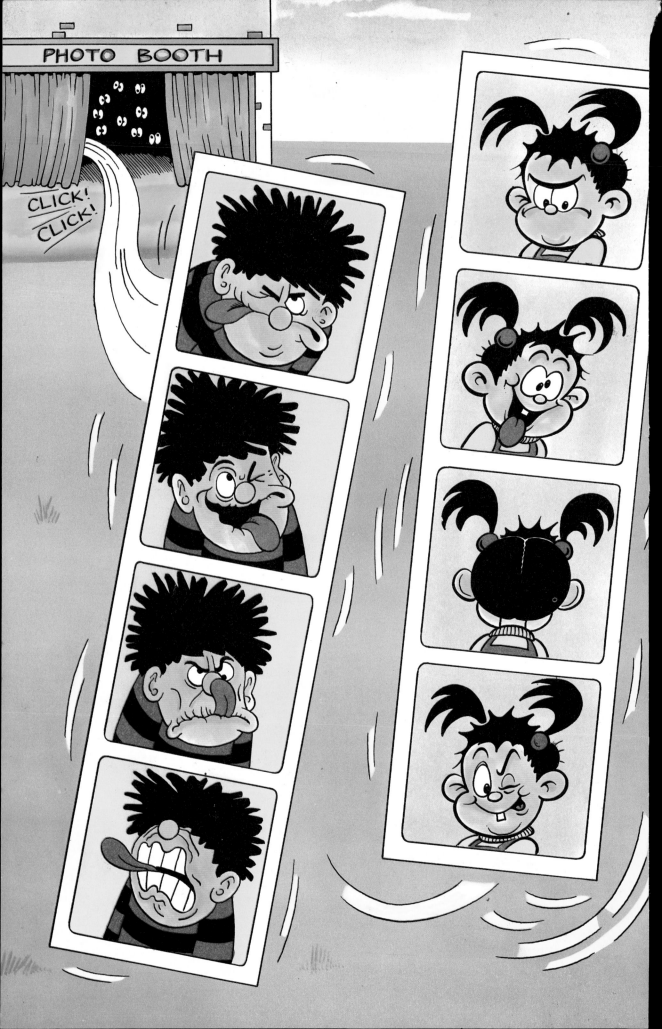